Let's Be

Nice

Written by Brad and Jim Tonner
Illustrated by Brad Tonner

ISBN: 0997412550
ISBN-13: 978-0-9974125-5-0
Library of Congress Control Number: 2018907427

TwinDesigns
Bristol, New Hampshire

Jim and Brad Tonner
Mother's Day 1961

To
COLE
SADIE
AND
ALI

ALL THE BEST
Jim AND BRAD
TONNER

Let's Be Nice

Written by Brad and Jim Tonner
Illustrated by Brad Tonner

Each day we have many choices to make.
To be nice should always be your first choice.

Let's be nice and pick some flowers for a friend.

There is someone new in school.
Let's be nice and ask them to join us for lunch.

4

You may not always agree with someone, let's be nice and just be friends.

Let's be nice and send someone a card
to brighten their day.

8

You are eating a yummy treat.
Let's be nice and share it with a friend.

A friend tells you their hopes and dreams.
Let's be nice and dream together.

11

12

When someone comes to visit,
let's be nice and make them feel at home.

Let's be nice and honor all those
who keep us safe.

Let's be nice and never forget teachers
for all they do for us.

A friend of yours is having a bad day.
Let's be nice and give them a hug.

Tonight, let's be nice and all sit down
and have dinner together.

Let's be nice and make a surprise visit to someone we have not seen in awhile.

24

Let's be nice and make sure we include everyone
in all of our fun.

Mom just went shopping let's be nice and help her bring the bags into the house.

27

28

Let's be nice and remember to thank all
the people who keep us healthy.

Let's be nice and tell your friend
they look great!

31

32

Let's be nice and let someone know they did their best, win or lose!

You will find, that after a day spent just being nice,
when you put your head down
on your pillow at night,
you will drift happily off to sleep.

Sweet dreams
let's be nice!

35

Made in the USA
Middletown, DE
31 August 2021